Tread softly if you care to seek
In wooded glade or field,
The dappled fawn, so shy and meek,
Quite perfectly concealed.

Printed and Published in Great Britain by D. C. THOMSON & CO., LTD.,
185 Fleet Street, London, EC4A 2HS

£1.35

# THE ICE ROSES

HAVE you ever looked at the beautiful patterns Jack Frost paints on your window on cold mornings? In Scandinavia they call those patterns "Ice Roses" and this is how they got their name...

... Long ago, a young painter called Peter lived in the mountains. One day, when winter was turning to spring, he was walking in the forest...

These flowers are too early. It's not your time yet!

But they are so beautiful, Alicia—and so brave to come out this early.

Two pretty girls shouldn't be quarrelling like this. Spring is in the air. The sun is shining and winter will soon be gone. Let me draw you with these flowers.

I will not sit in the sun— and winter is not over yet. You win for today, sister— but I will be back.

I will sit for you, young sir. My name is Rosanna. But my sister will not return today.

My name is Peter. I don't mind who I draw today—it's such a beautiful day.

*And so Peter drew his first picture of Rosanna. But all too soon . . .*

It grows cold again. I must go. My sister was right—it is not yet my time. Perhaps later in the year we shall meet again.

But wait! Can't we meet again tomorrow?

*The next day was cold and the forest sparkled with frost . . .*

Hello, Peter. I hoped you would come into the forest. Would you like to draw my picture today?

I was hoping to meet Rosanna—where is she?

Rosanna couldn't come today. It's much too cold for her.

Oh, well, you're just as pretty, so I don't mind. But it is cold today. I'm glad it will soon be spring.

*Peter and Alicia met every day in the forest. But as spring drew near—*

You're very restless, Alicia. We'd better try again tomorrow.

How can I sit still in this heat? I'm melting.

*But the next day—*

I brought some flowers for you, Alicia! I'd like to draw you holding them. A spring-time picture. Alicia, are you there?

Hello, Peter!

Rosanna! You've come back!

I hope you like drawing me—and flowers. I like to have flowers all around me.

Rosanna and Alicia are both so beautiful—but in completely different ways.

*Spring turned into summer, and Peter and Rosanna spent more and more time together.*

Roses are my favourite flowers. It wouldn't be summer without them.

I wish it could be summer all the time then—so that you could always have roses.

She brings happiness to everyone just like the sun.

*But all too soon summer came to an end, and one day—*

Alicia! What are you doing here? Where is Rosanna? She promised to meet me so that I could finish this painting.

She gone—and she won't be back. You can paint me instead. I'm much more beautiful.

It's no use. I keep thinking of Rosanna—I love her too much to draw your portrait.

Rosanna, always Rosanna! Forget Rosanna and come with me. I can make you a prince.

A prince! I have no wish to be a prince. And I could never go with you as long as I love your sister. She is warm and gentle—I will wait for her.

*Winter was cold and hard . . .*

It's cold for May. I hope the spring comes soon.

Fool! You will regret rejecting me. I will have my revenge. Rosanna will never return.

JANUARY FEBRUARY

Spring won't come until the Princess Rosanna returns—and there's no hope of that.

Rosanna! You know of Rosanna! Where is she?

So this is what you meant! Well, I won't give in and go with you, Princess Coldheart!

She lies a prisoner in her sister's dungeon. And there she'll stay unless her sister relents. They were never friends but now they have quarrelled bitterly. And we must pay. There will be no summer for us.

*But when July came with more snow, Peter began to change his mind.*

When will Rosanna come back and send all the snow away?

Soon, I hope. I must do something. Rosanna would hate to see the children like this. Alicia is keeping her a prisoner because I rejected her offer. I must go and rescue her.

*And so, Peter made his way to the land of the Winter Princess.*

The Ice Palace! Soon Rosanna will be free!

Princess Alicia's palace? It lies five days' journey north of the forest— beyond the Frozen Lake. But no mortal has ever returned from that journey.

# A VET'S BEST FRIEND...

**I**N the British Isles there are probably more pet animals per head of population than in any other country in the world. They give pleasure and companionship to the old and lonely, and often provide the young with their first experience of caring for another living creature.

This first pet can also sow the seed which many years later blossoms into that well known answer to the question, "What would you like to do when you leave school?"—" If possible, something to do with animals."

Well, one possibility is that of the Registered Animal Nursing Auxiliary. The scheme was started in 1961 by The Royal College of Veterinary Surgeons as a means of improving the training of veterinary assistants.

To find out more about the career, we visited an animal hospital in Epsom, Surrey, where Sandy Louks, the senior R.A.N.A. at the practice, began by outlining the basic requirements needed by prospective trainees.

Firstly, applicants must be seventeen and hold either three O-level G.C.E. passes or equivalents including mathematics, or physical or biological science, English language and one other. The next step is to gain a position at an approved training centre. A list of such veterinary practices together with a booklet about the scheme can be obtained from The Royal College of Veterinary Surgeons, 32 Belgrave Sq., London SW1X 8QP.

At the beginning of the two-year course there are usually a large number of recruits. However, this number often drops off during the first year as trainees realise

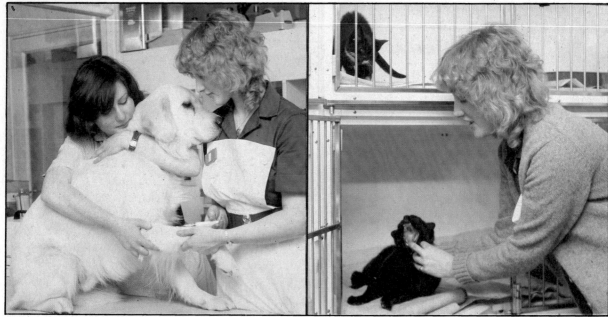

that the job does not just comprise of holding a playful puppy, but is a hard, tiring and often dirty job.

As with any job, the first-year trainees always have more of the unpleasant jobs to undertake. So it becomes their task to clean out the cages, swab the floor and generally clear up after the animals. Sandy pointed out that this is all part of the job, and even when qualified, these jobs have to be done, so it's best to get used to them in the beginning.

The girls at the Epsom practice work one of three eight-hour shifts. These tend to overlap so that at least one auxiliary is available whilst the veterinary surgeon is on duty and also prior to the surgery opening.

Sandy pointed out that the job is not of the nine to five variety and often they have to work beyond their basic hours. For example, recently, two puppies just a few days old were brought in which had to be fed every four hours—throughout the day and night. Happily the work was not in vain and both puppies survived.

**A** NORMAL working day starts with cleaning out the cages and feeding the animals that have been kept in overnight. A check is then made on their condition, and as in human hospitals, the details are entered on to a clip board fastened to each cage. The animals requiring surgery are then prepared for the veterinary surgeon.

There is always a variety of jobs to be done; from admitting animals, taking and developing X-rays, to anaesthetising patients and assisting in the operating theatre. In addition, there are the countless telephone queries, the preparation of laboratory samples and the collection of animals. These are not always straight-forward, like the time when the police rang up asking them to pick up a pig that was running amok on the local bypass!

With such a variety of jobs, the training has to be thorough, for a little knowledge is a dangerous thing.

During the first year the syllabus includes such subjects as anatomy, bacteriology, the working of bodily systems, hygiene and feeding. In addition there are the various pieces of diagnostic equipment plus the theory and practice of nursing to learn about.

At the end of the first year, trainees sit their preliminary practical and theoretical examinations and, if successful, graduate on to such advanced subjects as anaesthesia, radiography, surgical nursing and the birth and care of new-born animals.

After such a training it is not surprising that R.A.N.A.'s are thought of as a valuable addition to any veterinary practice, both in this country and abroad. Other opportunities for work also exist in universities and research establishments.

So if you are interested in animals, enjoy meeting people and are not afraid of hard work, a look at the R.A.N.A. scheme may put you in line for an interesting future with animals.

Why am I looking for my pal Lou with a trifle in my hand on my birthday? Well, I want to make sure she gets what's coming to her.

It all started when Lou heard her dad on the phone . . .

Right then, E. D. We'll expect you for dinner. 'Bye!

Eadie! Oh, no! My horrible cousin, Eadie is coming to dinner.

Lou left her house, deep in thought.

HUMPH! I can't stand Cousin Eadie. Fancy Dad inviting her to dinner. Just because she's a few years older than me, she thinks she can boss me about.

I must think of a way to make her feel most unwelcome, and she won't visit us again. There must be something I can do. What I need is an accomplice in crime . . .

. . . and I know just the right accomplice!

So, Lou arrived at Jinx's house, in the middle of a disco routine.

Hi, Jinx. What are you trying to do? You look like a windmill gone berserk.

You go and keep watch, while I sabotage the trifle.

SABOTAGE?

*Lou got started on the custard...*

There's nothing like a spot of soap powder to give custard a nice clean taste.

YEUCH!

Now to pour the custard over the trifle.

Don't forget the cherry on top.

SPLURGE!

*Later—*

I'd better get off home and let you get changed for dinner.

HUMPH! I'm not getting changed for Cousin Eadie! She might think she's welcome!

*But Lou's mum didn't agree.*

Lou, go and get changed for dinner. Your dad's boss is coming, so wear something pretty.

Oh, no! Dad's boss as well as Eadie. Now I won't be able to be rude to her.

*Later—*

Ah! There you are Lou! You actually look like a girl. Come and meet my boss.

I suppose he's talking to Eadie in the lounge.

Lou, this is Mr Dobson.

Hello, young lady. How nice to meet you.

Pleased to meet you, sir.

What a charming daughter you have, Mike.

Yes, she takes after her dad, E. D. Ho-ho!

Lou pondered . . .

E. D.? Dad calls his boss by his initials, E. D.

The penny dropped . . .

E. D. E . . D . . . EADIE . . . EADIE!

Excuse me, I'll go and help Mum.

Certainly, dear.

I must get rid of that sabotaged trifle!

Lou rushed to the kitchen . . .

Hey! That looks like the trifle the cat's eating. Phew! That's one way of getting rid of it.

SLURP!

After dinner . . .

What a lovely dinner!

Why thank you, E. D.

Mum didn't mention the missing trifle. So I won't say a word about it either.

*That night—*

Wait till I tell Jinx about E. D.! What a laugh.

*Next day, at Jinx's house—*

Happy birthday, Jinx.

Gosh, thanks. Feels like a book!

DEBBIE ANNUAL

*Lou told Jinx all . . .*

GIGGLE!

Jinx, Lou! Tea's ready!

*The birthday tea was great, until the trifle . . .*

YEEACH!

Is there something wrong with the trifle, girls? Lou's mother made it specially, and brought it over yesterday.

EEYUCK!

LOU'S MOTHER MADE IT! YOUR SABOTAGED TRIFLE!

'Bye! I'm off!

I'll teach you to trifle with me, you 'orrible creature!

MERCY! Remember, I'm your pal!

# Debbie Superpets

# TRIXIE'S TREASURE CHEST

IN Trixie Robbins' attic there was a chest full of mysterious and magical things. It had once belonged to her seafaring grandfather who had collected the strange objects from all over the world. One day . . .

Mm! This looks interesting. Wonder what's inside?

A vanishing cabinet. Wonder if it works?

PRESTO VANISHING CABINET

*Seconds later—*

*Downstairs—*

And I never have to empty it.

Back home—

Gosh! It's a marvellous thing this.

I'll say it is!

Trixie! Did you know there was another lid on the bottom?

But, when Dad opened the box—

BUZZ-ZZ! BUZZ! BUZZZ!

HUH! Marvellous thing indeed. That's the best place for it.

Sorry, puss, I can't go much further. The bushes are growing too close.

A kind of maze! Fantastic! No one said there was one near here. It's no good, puss, you'll have to go on alone. The wheel-chair can't possibly get through.

He's gone! I wonder what that blaze of light is? It's almost magical. It must be a reflection. But from what?

*In the following days, Helen saw the maze twice more.*

It's a kind of maze. Honestly, the cat leads me to it.

I haven't seen one. Come to that, I haven't seen any cat. But it's lovely to see you looking happier and better.

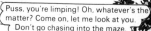

*Next day . . .*

Puss, you're limping! Oh, whatever's the matter? Come on, let me look at you. Don't go chasing into the maze.

He won't come! He's going in. Why? He looks back so pleadingly. Oh, puss, I can't follow.

Puss! Come back!

He's gone into the centre! The light's brighter than ever. What's happening? I can't see, sitting down.

He's not limping! He's dancing about in the light! The light—it seems to have cured him.

*Helen found a stout stick—*

Supposing it cures me too? I'm sure that's what he means. I—I must reach the light at the centre. I must!

*Meanwhile . . .*

Wherever is she? She must have wheeled herself right into the grounds.

Tea, Helen!

Helen! Helen! Where are you?

Mum! Her chair—it's empty! Oh, no!

She can't have left it! She hasn't walked since the accident.

But . . .

I'm almost there! The light! I'm going to reach it!

Oh, puss! Puss! I've walked! I've really walked! You made me—you showed me.

Helen! Helen!

Mum, Helen's walking! I can't believe it!

Oh, Helen, we knew you could if you really tried.

I followed the cat through the maze. There was this magical light and—

What maze? You mean, the bits of bushes and shrubs?

*Mr Milby investigated—*

The light could have been caused by sun reflecting from this old bottle. It makes sense. But by no stretch of imagination is it at the centre of a maze.

*Helen never found the maze again, and at the end of the family's stay—*

I never imagined anything. Anyway, I can walk! I don't really need a stick. That proves it.

We won't argue. I think it was something magical, too. It's been a marvellous holiday.

*But, as the car drew away . . .*

There's my cat! Old puss! He's seeing me off. He works the magic at Cat's Eye Cottage. I just know it!

# DON'T LAUGH AT SUZI

I wish the boys would let me have a game of football —just once.

Hey, Derek! Your sister's always hanging around. Why not let her join in?

What? You've got to be joking, Dave. She's hopeless!

HUH! It's just not fair. I hate being a girl.

*After the game—*

I see Suzi's still with us.

Yeah! I'm really fed up of that. It's time I said something.

Look, Suzi. We're sick of you tagging along all the time.

That's right! Go home and play with your dolls!

That was pretty rotten. She wasn't doing any harm.

Hey! What's this then, Dave? Getting soft in your old age?

Looks that way— doesn't it?

Oh, get lost you lot!

If only they'd understand how much I want to play football.

*Next day—*

We'd better get in some real practice for our big match against the Youth Club on Saturday.

I know! They beat us last time, so we can't let that happen again.

*Later—*

Suzi's pretty good with that football.

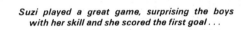
*Suzi played a great game, surprising the boys with her skill and she scored the first goal...*

*With five minutes to go the score stood at 2-2. Then Suzi scored the winning goal. After the match—*

# The Spirit Of Christmas

I LOVE Christmas, don't you? I think it's super, all the shops lit up, and the big tree standing up there in the market place and the turkey and the pressies ... oo, I don't know. Just about everything really.

I always go to the Carol Service. The one they hold round the tree. They give everybody a little lighted candle to hold, and it looks lovely, everyone standing there singing like mad and these little coloured lights moving about in the darkness.

This year they made a mistake and gave me two. One in each hand. I had to giggle to myself. I mean the man was so busy bending over the box he never even noticed.

Well, you could tell he didn't because when the music started I noticed that a boy near me hadn't got a candle at all, and he looked really miserable. I knew he was different from all the other boys at the service.

I tried edging along a bit to give him one of mine but there was this little kid in front who just wouldn't move. He kept staring at me. I made a really ugly face but he wasn't a bit put out.

He started laughing, in fact, and I heard his mum tell him to be quiet, but he couldn't stop. She shook him and he grabbed hold of her hand and pointed at me but she wouldn't turn round.

I could tell she was one of those people who only saw what they wanted to see and she certainly wouldn't have been interested in a girl like me. So I winked at the little kid and straight away he winked solemnly back and then stepped out of the way so that I could get through to the boy and give him one of my candles.

When I was close to him, I nearly forgot to give him one, because I was so taken aback. I mean, I hadn't realised he was so dishy. Dark, and with beautiful brown eyes. I took a deep breath and then remembered the candle.

"Hi," I said. "You can have this. I seem to have a spare."

"Thanks," he grunted, taking it. He didn't look at me, though. He was staring across at a dark-haired girl on the other side of the tree. She was one of those lucky people who even look pretty when they're singing—with their mouths wide open I mean—and she was really belting the carol out.

"Hark The Herald Angels Sing", I think it was. Though I've got to be honest, it could have just as well been "The Holly And The Ivy". I mean, not all of us can have a true ear for music, can we?

"You seem a bit down," I said to the boy.

He turned then, and really looked at me.

"Better than being up all the time," he grinned. "That's dead boring. I like change."

"Oh, me too," I hastened to agree. Having got his interest I was determined not to lose it. "I like

this town, don't you? Have you been here long?"

"Quite a while, actually."

His eyes went back to the dark girl. The carol had finished and she was turning the sheet over to find the next one. As she did so, the flame of her candle blew out, and now where she had been standing there was just a little pool of shadow.

"Hey, how did that happen?" the boy asked. "There's hardly any wind at all."

"Probably someone breathing a bit too hard," I suggested.

"Oh, yes," he muttered, suspiciously.

"You know her?" I ventured, being sure that he did.

"Mm," he said.

"She's very pretty," I sighed. I could tell he was really gone on her.

"I've tried and tried," he went on, as if talking to himself, "but she doesn't even notice me."

"It's as if you don't exist," I said sympathetically. "I know exactly what you mean. And at Christmas you always kind of expect miracles to happen, don't you. It's only natural after all."

"You know you've got a really understanding nature." He sounded surprised.

"Well," I said as modestly as I could, "I do like to see people happy. I mean, it's what we're here for, isn't it. Look, I think someone's passed your lady-friend a candle. She's all lit up again."

S HE was. The boy who'd handed her his candle was leaning very close to her so that both of them could read the carol sheet under the glow of that one single, yellow flame. Only they weren't looking at any piece of paper. They were looking at each other.

"Must be her boyfriend," I said, as casually as I could.

"They'd quarrelled!" he snapped back.

"Well, yes. That's why you were sent here," I told him. "Isn't it?"

"Huh," he snorted. "They'd never have found an excuse to make it up, if someone hadn't blown her candle out in the first place!"

"That's true," I agreed with a knowing smile.

"You did it!" he growled.

"Yes," I admitted. "I mean, you'd overstayed your time. That's

why I was sent. To see you'd put things right."

"What a cheek!" he muttered.

"It has to be a Happy Christmas for everyone," I reminded him. "You know the rules. You were supposed to see they made friends again."

"Okay, okay," he said. "Well they have, haven't they?"

We both looked across at the boy and girl. You could see they only had eyes for each other, and I was glad, because I honestly don't like working overtime, specially at Christmas.

Besides, there was a party going on back home. I didn't want to miss it. They'd be expecting us. And the carol service was almost over.

I hadn't realised it, but the boy had been watching me.

Now he smiled. Really smiled. Golly, he was dishy.

"You know, you're quite a looker yourself," he said. "Hadn't noticed before. What say we take off? Together, I mean."

"Good idea," I said. "One two three and . . ."

We rose in the air together. A perfect pair. No one noticed us, except the little kid I'd pulled a face at. His mouth dropped with a gasp of astonishment. He tugged at his mother's arm but she just shook him off, looking cross.

Like I said before, people only see what they want to see, don't they? I gave him a little wave and he waved back.

"You've made his Christmas," the boy said as we came to rest on a feathery white cloud. He still had hold of my hand, but I didn't say anything.

"It's given to very few," I said. "The Spirit of Christmas I mean. Look how hard we work to bring people together at this time of the year. Well, some of us anyway."

He had the grace to blush.

"Hey, come on!" I stood up, pulling him up with me. "Look, down there! The bells are ringing! It'll soon be Christmas Day!"

We watched for a minute or two, and then quietly we stepped to the edge of the cloud and took off into space again. I mean we had our own Christmas Party to go to, the one where we all met—some of us for the first time—to compare notes for the coming year.

Oh yes, we really enjoyed ourselves I can tell you. It was almost what you might call a very spirited affair . . .

# Teaser Time

Many of you will use these every day, but can you recognise them in close-up?

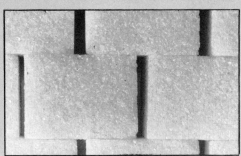

Here's a challenge that's fun, too. Try to solve this ketchup maze by entering at the arrow at the bottom left and working your way to the exit arrow at the top right.

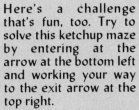

To which part of the map does the detail at the top left corner correspond?

These two pictures may look alike, but there are eight differences between them. Can you spot them?

Take a look at this close-up picture of a familiar object. Can you tell what it is?

But—

Oooh!

Hylda! Your ankle—

*The team doctor examined Hylda's ankle . . .*

I can't tell without an X-ray, Hylda, but I fear you may have chipped a bone in your ankle.

Oh no! If that's the case, that ruins my chances for the Olympics!

*The doctor's diagnosis was unfortunately correct and the closest Hylda got to the Olympics was on TV, in the caravan she shared in Seapool with the old lady she called Aunt Emma.*

This girl is good, Hylda, but I'm sure you could do better.

Oh, Aunt Emma! That's Magda Maranoci from Rumania. She's reckoned to be the best in the world!

Just look at her on the mat as well. She's tops at everything!

*And Magda did in fact win the Gold Medal.*

Well, she won all right, but I still think you could have beaten her.

I hardly think so, but it's nice of you to say it. We'll never know anyway.

*A week later, Hylda went along to visit some relatives whose circus had arrived in Seapool.*

SANTOR'S CONTINENTAL CIRCUS

I wish Aunt Emma hadn't said that about me being able to beat Magda Maranoci. I've been feeling unsettled ever since. Maybe Uncle Igor will be able to cheer me up.

We heard about the accident to your ankle. What a pity. Is it better yet?

Yes, Uncle Igor. It's fine now—but I missed my gymnastics, and the chance to get into the Olympic team. I've been feeling pretty miserable about that.

What you need is a holiday— away from here and its memories. And I know the very thing—you can come with us when we leave Seapool—to Rumania. Who knows, you may even meet the Maranoci girl!

Not much chance of that, but I don't care. Uncle Igor, you're a marvel—I feel better already.

*And so, three weeks later, Hylda and Aunt Emma found themselves in a hotel overlooking the Black Sea, as guests of Santor's Continental Circus.*

Oh, Hylda, this is lovely! Your Uncle Igor is wonderful!

I know and we can see his circus from our balcony here. We can go and visit him any time we want.

*Hylda was able to repay Uncle Igor in some small way by doing a floor routine for the circus . . .*

Oh, well done, Hylda! Wonderful!

*Several days later, as Hylda and Aunt Emma were returning from the beach—*

Golly, what's that crowd doing at our hotel?

Gosh, it's Magda Maranoci! Looks as if she might be staying at our hotel for a while!

*Hylda asked the manager about it . . .*

Yes, it is a great honour for us. Miss Maranoci comes here for a short holiday to recover from her magnificent efforts in the Olympic Games.

I know how she must feel. She should enjoy herself here.

*But, next day—*

Gosh, what's Magda doing in the hotel lounge on a super sunny day like this? And she looks so lonely. I'll see if I can speak to her and maybe cheer her up.

*Magda had a good command of English and the two girls were soon chatting happily.*

So you are a gymnast, too! I wish I had your freedom to come on holiday alone. Here, everyone is so protective about me. For my own safety, they say, I am not allowed to mix with other people.

Golly, what a life! You poor thing!

Catch my legs and help me over the rail, Magda!

I feel so much safer now that you are here. But how are we going to get down?

By the way I came up. Don't worry I'll help you.

And so—

This is a fairly simple circus trapeze movement. I'll start you swinging and let you go at the right moment. Don't look down towards the ground and you'll be all right.

If you say so, Hylda—but I am terrified.

**Everything worked out as Hylda had planned . . .**

. . . with Hylda swinging down herself after Magda had safely landed.

**Magda Maranoci's coach and bodyguards were quickly on the scene . . .**

Thank you, Miss Santor, for your help. Come, Magda—we must see immediately that you have not suffered some injury.

Just a moment, Madame Bogdanovic—please.

My people will not say too much about this incident and as I may never see you again, I would like to give you something to remember me by—you really deserve it.

Oh, Magda, how could I forget meeting the best gymnast in the world?

**When Magda had gone—**

She's given me her Olympic Gold Medal!

She said you deserved it. After tonight, she knows who is the best gymnast in the world!

# ARE YOU THE PRACTICAL TYPE?

## A SUPER FUN QUIZ FOR YOU TO TRY

Have you every wondered just how good you'd be in an emergency? Maybe you think you'd cope pretty well—or are you so sure you couldn't cope, that you just hope to keep well away from situations where your help might be needed! Either way, or somewhere in between, this quiz could save you a lot of future problems! It'll tell you just how pratical you really are, and it's packed with all kinds of info, that you might find very useful any moment now! So grab a pencil, and find out just how practical your ideas really are!

1. You were baking a cake as a surprise for your mum, who's out on a mammoth shopping expedition, but you get called away to a phone call at a crucial moment and the result is . . . one burnt cake! Would you . . .

   A. Feed the birds with it, and quickly bake another one?
   B. Cut the burnt bits off, and cover it with icing?
   C. Cut the burnt bits off and hope she won't notice?
   D. Hide it in a cake tin, thinking that when it's stale it can be used up in a trifle?

2. You've been walking a neighbour's dog to help her while she's in bed sick, but unfortunately Fido got away from you in the park and had a lovely swim in a smelly pond! He really smells horrible, but you don't have any dog shampoo and you don't want to bother your neighbour, so you give him a bath using . . .

   A. Some of the family's bath salts.
   B. Washing-up liquid.
   C. Ordinary shampoo.
   D. Plain water—with a dash of cologne added!

3. You have a paper round, and one of the houses on your route takes such a lot of newspapers, magazines and comics that it takes an age to push them through the letterbox. While you're at it, you're aware that somebody seems to be lying, very still, in the hall—though it's hard to be sure, through the ribbed glass in the door. Knocking on the door brings no answer. Would you . . .

   A. Ring 999 for an ambulance, as soon as you can?
   B. Knock up one of the neighbours and tell them?
   C. Tell the newsagent as soon as you get back, and let them handle it?
   D. Try and get into the house through a back way?

4. Mum's been saying lately that you never seem to do any job properly, so you're determined to make a success of the Saturday lunch you offered to prepare. The trouble is, with so many things to do, you can't remember if you put salt in the potatoes or not? So you decide to . . .

   A. Put just a little bit more in, to be on the safe side.
   B. Mash them when they're cooked, then you can taste the mash and if it's not salty enough, you can sprinkle a little into it.
   C. Taste the water they are cooking in, and only add salt if it isn't salty.
   D. Don't put any more salt in, and hope for the best.

5. Mum asked you to get a few items of shopping while you were out, but you spent longer on your own affairs than you realised. The shops will be closing in five minutes, and now you can't find her shopping list! Would you . . .

   A. Phone home, even though by the time you get back, the shops may be closed?
   B. Get a few of the things she often asks you to buy, and hope you've guessed right?
   C. Get one or two things that you remember were on the list, and don't worry about the others?
   D. Buy her some flowers and chocolates instead?

6. You were hurrying to finish something you were knitting or sewing for a birthday present, needed today, and somehow you've cut your finger! It won't stop bleeding, and even oozes through the sticky-plaster you put on. You don't want blood-stained work, so you . . .

   A. Rush out to buy a present instead.
   B. Put on several more plasters and a bandage, even though this makes it awkward to work.
   C. Wear rubber gloves.
   D. Wait until the cut dries up before continuing.

7. You and your friend are larking about in her kitchen and a vase of her mother's accidentally gets broken. Your friend puts the bits in the bottom of the dustbin and says it doesn't matter—but you notice she seems to be trying to hide the evidence! Would you . . .

   **A.** *Feel you have to buy a replacement?*
   **B.** *Say it'll be better all round if you, yourself, tell her mum what's happened and offer to go halves on buying a new vase?*
   **C.** *Fish the bits out and try to glue them together?*
   **D.** *Say and do nothing?*

8. You've gone on an outing to the seaside with a friend, and now she's looking awfully green and says she feels sick, after several ice creams and a good few rides on the roller coaster! Do you . . .

   **A.** *Find the nearest First Aid hut on the beach, and get her there as quickly as you can?*
   **B.** *Tell her she'll be all right if she takes things easily, and find her a quiet place to rest, out of the sun?*
   **C.** *Tell her she'll probably feel better if she IS sick, and get her to the nearest loo, where she can be ill in private?*
   **D.** *Keep telling her she looks fine, and hope that you'll soon see one of the adults in the party, so you can hand her over to them?*

9. It's your birthday, and you're having a large party. Now you're very embarrassed to receive an expensive present from a girl you haven't included in your invites! Would you . . .

   **A.** *Take her an invitation personally, and explain it wasn't sent before because somehow or other this evelope got missed?*
   **B.** *Don't invite her to the party, but remember to buy her something very nice when her birthday comes round?*
   **C.** *Just send off an extra invitation to her, without comment?*
   **D.** *Feel you can't hurt her feelings by sending her a late invite, so invite her to tea round at your house on another day?*

10. A favourite piece of jewellery gets accidentally put into the washing machine and comes out very battered. Would you . . .

   **A.** *Blame your mum for not noticing it was in the pocket of your jeans?*
   **B.** *Feel a bit annoyed, but realise it was your own fault?*
   **C.** *Decide that it's no use crying over spilt milk and forget about it?*
   **D.** *Wear the jewellery, battered though it is?*

# THEN ADD UP YOUR SCORES . . .

. . . if you find that 'A' ANSWERS come top of your list, you may be surprised to learn that though YOU think you are very practical and a real gem in an emergency, WE aren't quite so sure! You see, you have a terrific urge to do something, as soon as you spot things going wrong . . . and sometimes it really is better not to jump in too quickly! You are naturally warm-hearted, affectionate and impulsive, so it is very hard for you to learn to be cool and keep your head, specially when friends are involved, but take it from us, you'll be a lot more help in a sticky situation if you think it out really carefully before taking any action, however well-meant! For instance, in question 3 you could easily be mistaken (it might be a bundle of washing in the hall!) and a house taking so many comics and magazines is less likely to contain just a solitary person, so it really would be best to try to get some other kind of help before calling out an ambulance, which might be needed more urgently elsewhere. We think, with your concern for others, you'll want to improve your reactions to emergencies, and by looking through the B and C answers we think you'll find some helpful tips.

If you're a girl who chose mainly 'B' ANSWERS, then you are probably rather quiet and shy, and may worry that in an emergency, you wouldn't know what to do. Well, we can reassure you! You certainly have all the right ideas, and use plenty of common sense in sticky situations. We think that when you've had just a little bit more experience, you'll have all the answers at your

tingertips! To help you along, read the quiz again, and note that the C answers are more practical to the situations in questions 2, 4, 5, 6.

'C' ANSWERS indicate a girl who is practical, full of common-sense, but not very imaginative! This makes you a good person to have around in a crisis, but there are occasions when your reactions, though sensible, may occasionally cause problems you hadn't thought of, as in question 7 (your friend might think you're trying to get her into trouble!) and question 8, where though well-meaning, all your talk and rush might make your pal sick, whereas if you'd just kept her cool and quiet, she might have recovered! Try reading the quiz again, and look at the B answers, which are often a good alternative and show a bit of imagination . . . which you occasionally lack!

Then we come to the people who've picked mostly 'D' ANSWERS—D for Ditherer, as it happens! You have a lot of imagination, and you get very concerned about problems and sticky situations, but instead of taking a practical attitude, your concern just side-tracks you and gets you into even more involved situations. We can see some VERY sticky situations arising if you chose D for for question 3, for instance! The best advice we can give you is to ask yourself, when trouble arises, what alternatives there are, and think them through carefully before deciding what to do. There is nearly always a fairly simple thing which you can do, which at the very least won't make the problem any worse . . . unlike a few of your answers! Read the B and C answers, and you'll find these are a lot less likely to lead to trouble than your own selection!

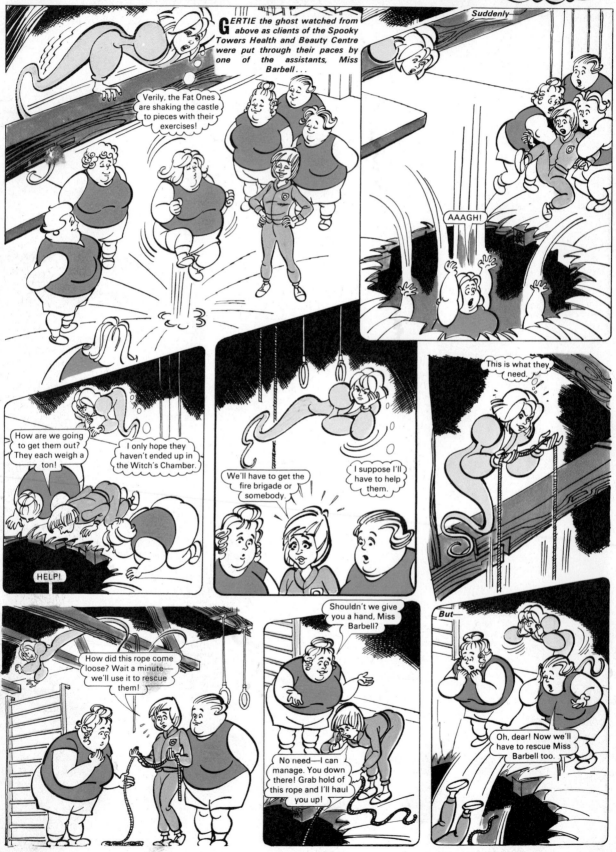

# What's Cooking?

If Mum thinks you're old enough, how about giving her and the family a real treat and cooking Sunday lunch?

The menu given here is quite simple to prepare but is guaranteed to be quite delicious!

As always, don't embark on any cooking without getting Mum's permission.

## METHOD OF WORK

1. Make dessert first, and leave in fridge to set.
2. Make soup up to point before vegetables are added. Scrub potatoes, put on baking tray, place in pre-heated oven 400 deg. F., or Gas mark 6. Allow 1-1½ hours to bake, depending on size of potato.
3. Carry on with soup.
4. Prepare broccoli.
5. Whip cream for dessert.
6. Place pork under grill
7. Put plates in oven to warm.
8. Make cream sauce.

## GREEN PEA SOUP

1 large tin garden peas
1 large onion—chopped
1 leek—cut lengthwise, and sliced
2 large carrots
Small piece of turnip
2 pints stock (made by dissolving 2 ham stock cubes in boiling water)
Knob of butter
Seasoning

1. In a large pan melt your knob of butter. Add your onion and leeks. Cook over a moderate heat for 5 minutes.
2. Add your stock, peas and seasoning. Simmer for about 15 minutes.
3. While this is simmering, slice your carrots and turnip into roughly quarter inch cubes.
4. Add your vegetables, and cook for a further 45 minutes.
5. Just before serving, garnish with a little chopped parsley.

## Menu

### (FOR FOUR)

GREEN PEA SOUP
* * *
PORK WITH CREAM SAUCE, BAKED POTATOES, BROCCOLI
* * *
YOGHURT FLUFF

## PORK WITH CREAM SAUCE

4 pork steaks or fillets
1 large onion
4 oz. mushrooms
Small carton double cream
1 teaspoon dried rosemary
3 oz. butter

1. Place a knob of butter on each piece of meat, season, and place under moderate grill. Grill for about 10 minutes each side, depending on thickness of meat.
2. Peel and chop onion. Wash and slice mushrooms (do not peel them as most of the flavour is in the skin).
3. In a small frying pan, or heavy based saucepan, melt 2 oz. of the butter.
4. When quite melted, add the onions, mushrooms and rosemary. Stir, and allow to cool for 10 minutes.
5. Add the cream, mix well, and simmer for a further 5 minutes, being careful not to let it come to the boil. Pour this over the pork steaks just before serving.

## YOGHURT FLUFF

1 pkt. lemon jelly
1 carton lemon flavoured yoghurt
Carton double cream

1. Make up jelly as on packet.
2. When cool, add yoghurt, whip well. Put in fridge to set.
3. When cold decorate with whipped cream.

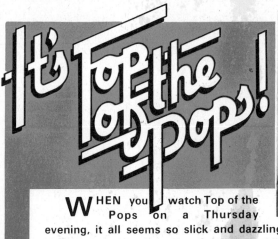

# It's Top-the Pops!

*ABBA*

**W**HEN you watch Top of the Pops on a Thursday evening, it all seems so slick and dazzling. Lots of bands performing their hits, Legs and Co kicking their way through a top tune, and linking it all together, one of our favourite disc-jockeys rattling out the introductions with split-second timing.

Do you ever wonder how it's done? How this kind of programme is put together? When you think that each week's Top Thirty is only announced on Tuesday, and that Top of the Pops is recorded on Wednesdays, you begin to realise what a terrific rush it all is—and how many headaches are in store each week for the production team!

Monday morning finds the producer studying the charts, trying to find out from his spies and contacts which records are selling well, and sorting out various video films which have been sent in by promoters. Abba or Blondie, for example, who often can't appear live are very conscious of their fans. So when they release a new single, a film is made of them singing it and a copy sent to Top of the Pops to promote the record.

On Tuesday morning, there's a deadly hush as the production team listens to the new chart run-down, provided by the British Market Research Bureau. The Top Thirty records are identified by taking a sample of various record shop sales. But just which shops they are, is a closely-guarded secret!

Once they know the new chart, the Top of the Pops team can get cracking. They only use records which are going up the charts, so all those dropping down are forgotten right away. Obviously, the aim is to get as many bands as possible into the studio. Believe it or not, about an hour after the new chart is announced, the Top of the Pops team has produced its plans and running order.

Of course, all the record companies are eager to get their discs featured so the telephones at the TV centre are jangling ceaselessly on Tuesday morning. If bands can't make appearances in person—maybe they're on tour or playing a concert—they've *LEGS and CO* usually sent in a video film which is used.

*LEGS and CO*

On Wednesday, the floor manager is supervising things in the studio itself: making sure the bands don't dump their equipment in the wrong place. He's constantly in touch with the production control room—a sort of gallery above the studio, with a battery of TV screens—one for each camera used.

Then the rehearsals begin. The bands themselves don't come to these rehearsals. Instead there are stand-ins, who act the part of the bands. And later when the band is actually performing, the same guys work clearing paths through the audience for the zooming cameras.

*BLONDIE*

# It's Top of the Pops!

*PETER POWELL*

There's no audience till Wednesday evening, though. At the earlier rehearsals the camera crew needs empty space to roll around. Some of the five cameras are huge, and they can extend way up in the air above the heads of the audience for high shots. Being a BBC cameraman certainly isn't a job for a chap with vertigo!

All the camera shots are worked out in detail, and each cameraman makes a note of his shots on a clipboard attached to the side of his camera. Up in the gallery, one of the producer's assistants calls out the camera numbers and the shots which are coming up.

Around midday, they're usually rehearsing the Legs and Co number. A week before, choreographer Flick Colby helps to choose a likely chart-climber for her girls to dance to. Their numbers are picked a week ahead so there's more time to work out and practise a routine. Sometimes, though, if the chosen number drops right out of the charts, Flick and her girls have to scrap their planned routine and work out another—in twenty four hours!

All afternoon there are rehearsals, then at 5 pm, a full run through. By now the show's usually slipping along very smoothly. But if things do go wrong during the evening recording, everything can stop while they re-record and get it right. It's one of the advantages of recording programmes.

In the old days, though, things weren't like that. Top of the Pops used to be broadcast live—and that made everything much more hair-raising! Top of the Pops started fifteen years ago, and in the early days, the studio atmosphere was electric—and suffocating!

There used to be a sea of dancing teenagers, but now fire regulations cut the audience down in size—only 120 are allowed, and in the vast BBC studios that's only a thin sprinkling. And by law, they must all be over the age of sixteen. A bit of a problem for the BBC ticket unit staff who issue all the tickets!

Well, at 7.15 p.m. the studio is invaded by the audience, and the magic moment arrives. This time, instead of stand-ins, there's the 'real thing'. The D.J., Peter Powell perhaps, introducing the programme, and groups like The Police thrashing about in the dazzling lights. The studio audience dodge the rolling cameras, gaze at their idols, and try to wriggle into camera shots so they can watch themselves on TV when Top of the Pops is broadcast next day.

When the occasional video tapes are used, the studio lights go dim and the atmosphere relaxes for a moment. Down in the studio audience, you can hear the track that's being recorded, but you can't see the film. So it's a time for wandering about, and maybe spying on the other artists who are ready to come on.

Top of the Pops has certainly changed since it began—from being overcrowded and unpredictable, it's become super-slick, super-smooth and almost super-sonic! But whatever else has changed, one thing hasn't. The Top of the Pops team work themselves into a frenzy every week to bring you the best of the bang up-to-date Top Thirty.

*THE POLICE*

# Debbie Superpets

Yes, My name's Martin Lomax, and I'm a naturalist. I've moved into the old cottage across the valley. I intend to study wildlife there. I'm building up a collection of animals.

Super! Perhaps I could come and see them some time?

*Just then—*

Here comes Evan Price. He farms near us. He looks upset about something.

Gwen, I know Meg is to be trusted, but have you seen any stray dogs about? I've found two of my sheep savaged.

That's terrible. I haven't seen any dogs, but I'll come with you and take a look round, Mr Price.

I'd better be going.

It was a pretty savage attack, Mr Price.

Yes, it took a big dog to kill the sheep like that.

Meg's picked up a scent. And she doesn't like it! Show us the way, Meg.

She's brought us back to the stream. But she's lost the scent. The dog we're following must have gone into the water.

There's a track here.

Hang on! Oh, Meg's going for the wolf! Be careful, Meg.

Help!

I've got you! Quick! Meg's in danger!

You're safe. Meg, look out! The wolf's going to spring!

*But Meg was too clever—*

Meg's dodged the wolf! And the wolf can't get a footing as it lands!

Meg's all right! The wolf's gone into the ravine. It was one of your animals, wasn't it, Mr Lomax?

Er—yes. I was studying it, but it broke out of its pen. I didn't want to start a panic, so I was trying to get it back secretly before it did any more damage.

*The next morning—*

Lomax has paid me for the dead sheep. And he's promised not to keep any more dangerous animals.

The legend about disaster following the Grey Wolf nearly came true. But Meg was a match for it, Mr Price!

## Girls in Uniform –
# A FAIR COP!

Whether you live in a small village or a large city, responsibility for law and order rests with the local bobby. In the Armed Forces, the upholding of the law is carried out by the Military Police.

As in the civilian service, women are playing an ever increasing role within the Military Police. Corporal Babs Whetman is a member of 160 Provost Company, Royal Military Police.

Like all new recruits to the Women's Royal Army Corps, Babs was given six weeks basic training before moving to Chichester for more specialised training. This meant having to learn self-defence.

Maintenance of her Land Rover was something Babs had to learn . . .

Physical fitness is very important in the Military Police, but the course also included such things as military law, police duties, first-aid, driving and map-reading.

. . . as well as how to direct traffic in the busy streets outside the barracks.

Civilian and military police work in close co-operation, and Babs often has to patrol the streets with the local bobby.

This is important as it helps to establish a vital link between the civilian and military authorities.

Being a member of the Military Police is not an easy job. Self-confidence, personality and patience are important qualities in handling tricky situations with tact, yet authority.

Her work involves looking after the horses, going out on patrol, appearing at ceremonial occasions and ensuring the security of firing ranges.

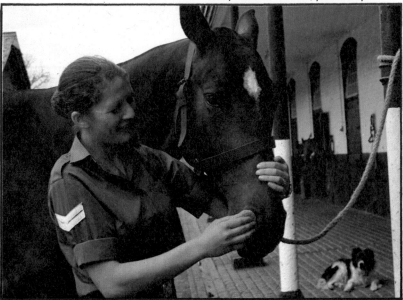

The Military Police is one of the few army units which still maintain a mounted troop. Competition to join is very keen and Babs' friend, Terrie, was one of the lucky ones.

*A job in the Military Police is not of the nine-to-five variety, but it's very rewarding, and there are plenty of opportunities for a busy social life. Women members of the Military Police, like other WRAC personnel, receive new postings every two years. Often they have the chance to work in Germany, Cyprus or Hong Kong.*

As you've got the letter, you can make the choice, Mary. We're off to town just now. 'Bye!

Well, thank you very much, I must say!

Mary made out a list of possible sports—

We're best at team games. I think we should beat Carver's at netball—yes that's it!

Mary picked up the list without being aware that she'd picked up Jill's letter, too—

Now I'll just cut out the word "netball" and send it in an envelope to Carver's.

What's that? Oh, it's just the wind blowing the window shut!

I'll deliver this to Carver's straight away. We'll soon show them they're not so great as they seem to think!

Hand this to your Third Form captain, please.

Back in the study—

Gosh! Here's the slip with netball on it! What did I put in that envelope?

Oh, dear, I see what has happened! I've challenged them to tiddlywinks instead!

# The Happiest Christmas Ever

"OH, come on, Clare," I said, as she pressed her nose even closer to the pet shop window, "we've got to get back or Gran will be wondering where we are. And anyway, I'm getting cold."

I pulled at her hand, and very reluctantly she walked away with me. I knew how much Clare longed for a puppy. I'd made her promise not to say anything to Gran about it, hoping she wouldn't guess.

Since Mum had died and we'd come to live with Gran nearly a year ago, I'd realised how really hard-up she was. She'd given up her job to look after us, although she'd never said a word about it. The last thing she'd want was another mouth to feed.

I tried to distract Clare's attention by pointing out the huge Christmas tree in the market. It really was lovely, all the fairy lights twinkling, and the beautiful white fairy standing on tiptoe at the very top.

I looked down at my sister and knew she was making a wish.

"Look," I said desperately, "let's go and see if we can buy Gran's present. We've just about enough money now."

Clare and I had been saving for ages to buy Gran a real silver chain to replace the one she'd broken on her silver locket. It had always hung round her neck for as long as I could remember.

It had been a present from Grandad. Somehow in my mind, when I thought of Gran I thought of the locket. So I was really anxious to get that chain for her for a present.

# The Happiest Christmas Ever

It cost every single penny we had, but when I saw it nestling in its cotton wool box I knew it was worth it. I could see Clare was pleased, too, and had forgotten just for that minute about the puppy.

And she didn't mention it again. I brought some coloured paper from school and we started making chains to hang up in the sitting-room.

A couple of days before Christmas, Gran and I put them up. Clare was still finishing her tea, so we left her to it and I climbed up on a chair to tack the decorations into a corner.

And that's when I noticed something odd. Clare wasn't eating her slice of fruit cake, one of her favourites. She was busy stuffing it into her pocket.

Before I could say anything, she suddenly got up and asked Gran if she could go out in the garden.

I watched her through the window as she trotted up the path. There she stopped, and looked round very carefully. Then she went into the shed. I was really intrigued because normally neither Clare nor I ever went there.

The only person who used it was Gran, who kept her gardening things there. And this time of the year she didn't need any of them.

But there was certainly something in there now that held a lot of interest for Clare. I looked across at Gran. She was humming to herself as she stuck some loose paper chains together, and I knew she'd hardly noticed Clare go out.

Well, I thought, I'll wait until later. When Clare's gone to bed.

IT was dark when I slipped out into the garden, shielding the light from my torch very carefully, so's I wouldn't attract attention.

I opened the shed door, and crept inside. Something soft and warm just threw itself at me, whining like mad.

I staggered back, and then straightened up.

It was a little brown puppy.

I picked it up and hugged it. I'd never have admitted it, but I had longed for one, just like my little sister. For a minute I held it really close, and then I set it down on its wobbly legs.

"Oh, Clare," I muttered to myself. "Wherever did you get him?"

I had a good idea what must have happened, though. He'd followed her home, and she'd hidden him here in the shed. I'd have to take him back to whoever he belonged to. I had to.

Only, when I tackled her she wouldn't tell me where he had come from. All she did was beg me to let her keep him, just till Christmas was over.

In the end, I hadn't the heart to say no. Maybe, a couple of days wouldn't matter. Just a couple. I'd save him some scraps and take him for walks when Gran was out shopping.

Except that the puppy had other ideas. Right on Christmas Eve, when Gran was helping Clare to hang an old stocking over the fireplace, there was this sort of scratching at the back door. Clare and I just looked at each-other. He'd escaped from the shed! Then he walked in.

Goodness knows how he'd managed to push the back door open, but he had. He just stood there on his four stubby legs, wagging his tail.

I didn't dare look at Gran. But when I did, she was smiling.

"I'm ever so sorry, Gran," I blurted out.

I started telling her the whole story, while Clare just looked at her, pleadingly.

"I think Santa sent him specially for us to keep," Gran said. She drew both Clare and the puppy on to her lap, then she looked up at me. "Clare found him in the shed, Molly, because that's where I hid him. He's my Christmas present to both of you."

"Oh, Gran!" I couldn't believe it. I hugged her shoulders. "But — but he must have been so expensive, and there'll be his food — "

"I sold my locket, love," Gran said simply. "It was no good without the chain, anyway. And that paid for quite a few tins of meat for him. We'll manage."

Silently, I went across to my satchel. I drew out the little paper parcel and held it out to her.

"From Clare and me, with love," I said. "Open it, Gran."

Her eyes were very bright when she saw the chain. Then she looked up at me. For a minute, I could've sworn there were tears in her eyes.

"Four of us now instead of three," she said. "And the most beautiful present you could have thought of. I'll never part with it . . . never. Oh, Molly, Clare, I've got a feeling this is going to be the happiest Christmas ever!"

# PICTURE, PICTURE ON THE WALL...

MANDY THOMAS lived with her parents in Grimeford, a drab town with few places for children to play and high, bleak factory walls.

It's a long way to the park isn't it, Dad?

Yes, Mandy, it's a pity that the piece of old waste ground at the end of our street couldn't be turned into a playground, but the Council say they've no money.

ALL WEEK the inn had been full to capacity, bursting at the seams with weary travellers. She had hardly had time to draw breath from rising before daylight to almost falling asleep on her cold, bare feet long after darkness had fallen.

Her only refuge was the old straw palliasse in the stables, her comfort the warmth and closeness of the animals.

And the star.

For weeks now it had hung, suspended like a flashing, many-faceted diamond, filling the open door of her sleeping place with its brilliant white light. No one else at the inn had remarked on it. Not Ephraim, the potman, or short-tempered, hard-handed Sarah.

"It's so bright," she said timidly to Ephraim, as she handed him the ale pots. "Like a great jewel."

"Jewel!" snorted Sarah. She kneaded the rough dough with such force that pieces flew from the table only to be gathered in again by her raw, red hands. " 'Tis a pity idle heads like yours can't be put to better use, girl! That fire needs minding! Quick — sharp!"

She dodged out of the way of Sarah's familiar sharp-boned elbow, and pattered across the kitchen floor, picking up the rush basket for the wood as she did so. But Sarah hadn't finished with her.

"And tonight you'll not see your precious star from the stable," she called. "For the master's given the new travellers the use of it. 'Tis the only place left in the whole of Bethlehem. You'll have to find somewhere else to sleep."

The animals, she thought as she bent to gather the first few sticks of kindling, would not like sharing with strangers. It worried her much, much more than the loss of her own bed. But worry was driven out of her mind by the rush of work that evening. And when at last she had finished, and the inn was shuttered and silent, she dragged her weary feet across the courtyard, forgetting just for that moment that the stable would be closed to her that night.

And then, nearing it, she heard a cry. At first she thought it was the new young lamb recognising her step and giving his usual welcome. But this cry was somehow different. A human sound.

A baby.

She stood to one side of the opening, her heart beating fast.

A baby lying in the manger, the cattle silent, staring, just like herself. The mother with head bent, the father at her side.

And gifts. Gifts for the new-born infant — she saw the glint of gold — lying by his side.

She longed to go in. Longed to touch the small hand, to press her own offering upon him as was the custom.

Turning, she stared back towards the inn. She had nothing. Nothing to give. The star above her head shone so brilliantly that the whole of the surrounding countryside seemed to light up. She could see the grass, the trees, the broken walls, the lanes beyond.

And she remembered the lilies. Bethlehem's wild lilies. Surely somewhere she could find a flower. Hidden, protected from the winter's bitter chill, there would be a bloom. Frantically, she searched.

But there was nothing. Sadly, she returned to the stable.

And again she saw the manger, again she dropped her eyes in wonder. And saw at her feet, springing from the frozen ground, a miracle.

A single flower.

She bent and snapped the slender green stem, then held the bloom close to her face.

A perfect star.

A perfect, pale white star.

The baby reached out its hands as she came close, and he touched the pale, waxy petals. And she was filled with such happiness that she knew that never again would she feel cold, or hungry, or frightened.

# LITTLE WHITE FLOWER

And all because
of the little white flower.
that was born the same night as
the baby in the manger. The flower
that has survived through the ages to
bring a touch of magic in the deep, dark days of
winter.

The Christmas Rose.

As pale and shy as the poor young servant girl
who first found it and brought it as the only gift
she could bring to a new-born infant . . .

# SAFFY and her PUPPIES

*THE PUPPY BOOK* © 1980 Camilla Jessel
*First published by Methuen*
*Children's Books Ltd., 1980*

**T**HIS is a true story—of Saffy, the labrador, and her puppies.

Before the puppies were born, Saffy searched for the best place to have them. Some ancient instinct made her want to dig a hollow in the earth and she chose the prettiest flower bed in the garden—but it was the wrong sort of bed!

Saffy finally settled for the special box she was given. This was lined with newspapers to make a good warm surface for the puppies and which could be thrown out when they got messy. To make it even more comfortable for the puppies, Saffy tore the newspapers to shreds.

**Based on THE PUPPY BOOK
by Camilla Jessel**

At last the puppies were born, one at a time, until there were nine in all. Saffy licked them clean and they were kept warm until the proud but tired mother could give them their first feed.

At first, the puppies wanted only their mother . . .

... but Saffy had to have a few short walks each day. While she was away, the puppies felt cold without her and huddled together for warmth.

The puppies were born with their eyes tightly shut.

They were unable to stand and slithered along, looking more like baby seals than dogs.

About a fortnight later, their eyes were completely open and they could almost walk, although their weak, wobbly legs bent under the weight of their bodies.

The puppies seemed to develop the instinct to fight almost as soon as they could stand, but they didn't hurt each other as they didn't have any teeth.

As they grew, the puppies had to get extra feeding and they soon learned to eat out of a bowl—

—but a dish of water proved a puzzling experience at first!

The puppies learned by their mistakes—like the greediest one who knocked over the breakfast jug, hoping for an extra feed. He got stuck!

The largest puppy could eat faster than the rest. He often managed to push away a smaller one and grab two dinners.

As the puppies grew older, they became more of a handful— stealing food when no one was looking, playing with toys which didn't belong to them, falling in the goldfish pond and having to be dried off!

As they cut more teeth, they were given large bones which would not chip or get stuck in their throats.

Gradually the puppies were sold—ten full-grown Labradors running round the house wouldn't leave room for anyone else! But two were kept and training started— unwillingly at first as the puppies didn't like being pulled along by the neck. But they quickly got the idea and were soon trotting happily ' at heel '.

And so,
after all the bustle and
excitement, life for the beautiful Saffy
settled down again into a quiet, more normal routine.

# Jenny Wren!

*Eighteen-year-old Jenny Fenton decided to follow in her mother's footsteps by joining the Women's Royal Naval Service, or the Wrens, as they are more popularly known.*

Jenny chose to become a meteorological observer—a weather forecaster—and after basic training, was posted to H.M.S. Seahawk in Cornwall, for her specialist training. This involved lots of lectures and film shows.

During her time in Cornwall, Jenny was taught how to describe the varying weather conditions and also how to gather information from the various pieces of meteorological equipment.

Here she studies a machine which gauges the amount of sunshine there is during a 24-hour spell . . .

. . . and a rather strange looking device on the airfield which measures rainfall.

Having gathered the information, Jenny then sends it by teleprinter to the Met. Office at Bracknell.

Jenny's work also involves preparing weather charts showing the various conditions all over the country.

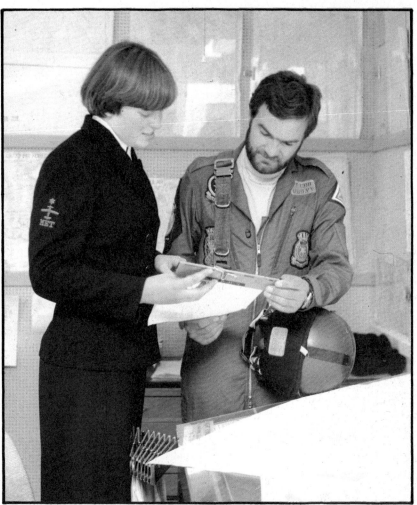

Accuracy and neatness are important as it is from these charts that aircrews are briefed for their flights.

Met. observers are encouraged to fly in order to gain a pilot's eye view of the weather and Jenny is seen here in the cockpit of a Hunter t

# Debbie Superpets

# Teaser Time

Take a good look at this photograph, before you decide what it is.

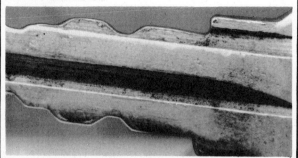

This household article looks different in close-up. Can you tell what it is?

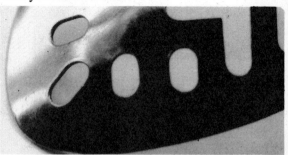

At first glance, these two pictures may look alike, but there are eight differences between them. Can you find them?

One of these designs is different from the rest. Which one is it?

Can you find your way through the maze from the arrow at the kitten's mouth to the exit at its ear?

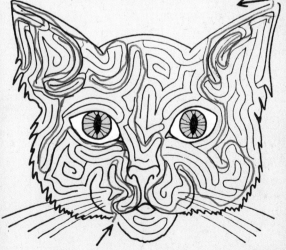

# Stella from the Stars

# The BIONIC HORSE

WHEN Sue Taylor's horse, Ben, was injured, he was healed by some space travellers in a flying saucer—and developed remarkable powers.

The village boys have been larking about in the old cottage again, by the looks of things. It's a dangerous place to play, Ben.

This place ought to be knocked down, but nobody seems to own it.

Suddenly—

Gosh! No sooner said than done with you, Ben!

Hello, that box looks new. It must have been hidden up in the roof timbers. Hang on while I take a squint, Ben.

The box is full of jewellery! I've seen Lady Morton wearing this diamond necklace. It was stolen from her house. I've discovered a thieves' hoard!

*Suddenly—*

Golly! The crooks have come back for their loot!

Hey! Put that box down, girl!

Move, Ben! They're not getting their hands on this stuff again! They're following! But they won't catch you, Ben. Hang on, though! Suppose we catch them? I reckon you could do it, Ben! Then we'll hand over the thieves and their loot!

Here's a good spot for an ambush, Ben.

Here they come! Now, Ben!

Aagh!

Hup!

She's coming back! Jumping like a grasshopper!

Get out quietly, or I'll set my horse on you! I'm taking you to the police station!

Bah! We are the police, you nutcase!

Detective-Sergeant Johnson! Here's my official card! We found that loot, and we were keeping watch to nab the thieves when they came back to collect!

Oh, dear! Er—a bit of a misunderstanding, sergeant!

*Later, back at Sue's home—*

I am Sheik Hassan. I hear you have a remarkable horse, girl. Kindly bring him out for me to inspect, before I buy him.

This is him, sheik! Ben's the only horse I've got. And you're right, he is pretty remarkable. He's not for sale, though!

I anticipated your reluctance. I will pay your price, and give you my best horse as well. A pure-bred Arab stallion.

That's certainly a magnificent stallion, sheik. But he's still not as special as Ben. You're wasting your time.

I challenge you! A contest between our horses. If you win, the stallion is yours. If my horse wins, I claim Ben!

A challenge? Well, I'm sure Ben would win.

*And so—*

A race across the common. My men have gone ahead to mark the course.

Right. Give the word, sheik.

*And they were off!*

What's that rolling out of the bushes? Gosh, marbles! Careful, Ben, they'll fetch you down!

*Ben changed direction quickly.*

*Minutes later—*

Aagh!

*Just then—*

A rope! Now they're trying to trip you, Ben!

*But Ben kept going.*

"Oof!"

"They won't stop you, Ben!"

"Aagh!"

"We're overtaking. But that groom's running the stallion to a standstill with his whip."

"Ben doesn't like the way you're treating that horse!"

"Ugh!"

"I claim the victory! My horse is home first!"

"Without a rider! Yes, I know Ben unseated him, but that's nothing to the tricks you tried to play on me!"

"My horse has collapsed!"

"He was ridden too hard! Help him, Ben."

"Electric flashes from your horse's hoof!"

"He's giving your stallion some of his own energy, and reviving him!"

"Ben's saved your stallion, but he's not too pleased with you, sheik! You'd better go before you upset him again."

"Yes, yes! Come, men! A horse that behaves like an electric tiger is too much for me! I withdraw."

# What's Cooking?

*Mash, chips and roast potatoes are all very well, but there's a lot more to our old friend the spud than these everyday dishes! In fact, when he gets his old brown coat off and is all dressed up to go to town, you'll hardly recognise him.*

*Remember, always ask Mum's permission before using the cooker.*

## POTATO OMELETTE

This is very quick! Just peel about 1 lb. (500 g.) potatoes, and grate them on the coarsest part of the grater. Beat three eggs with 1 tablespoon cold water and a pinch of salt and pepper, and stir in the grated potato. Heat a little oil in a frying-pan, and pour the mixture in. Cook quite quickly until set on the underneath, then turn the heat right down and put a lid on, to allow the potato to cook thoroughly. When the potato is soft, sprinkle grated cheese on top, and put under the grill for a few minutes to brown. This amount serves three or four people.

## TATTIE PUFF

You can use left-over mashed potato for this savoury snack, or cook some potatoes specially. You need to allow about one medium-sized potato per person. Mash the potatoes thoroughly, and for each helping add one tablespoon grated cheese and one teaspoonful milk (better still, use the top of the milk). When nice and soft, break an egg carefully into a cup and lift out the yolk only with a spoon. Beat that into the potato (one egg is enough for up to two helpings). Beat the remaining egg white until it is fluffy, with a pinch of salt and pepper, and then beat that into the potato mixture too. Butter the insides of individual ovenproof dishes, and mound up the potato inside, patterning the top with a fork. Bake at 400 deg, gas mark 6, for about 15 minutes if you used freshly cooked, hot potatoes, or half an hour if the potato was cold to start with.

## MURPHY'S CURRY

This is something spicy and different, to eat as a snack or even as a meal by itself, using left-over, plainly boiled potatoes, put about ½ oz. (12 g.) butter into a small pan with a level tablespoon flour, and 1-2 teaspoons curry powder (according to taste) and stir gently with a wooden spoon until well mixed. Remove from the heat. Carefully stir in ½ pint hot water (perhaps from cooking the potatoes) in which you have dissolved half a chicken stock cube, and then return to the pan to heat until the mixture bubbles. Remove from the heat. Cut the cooked potatoes into small cubes, and stir into the curry sauce. Add ONE of the following: 2 tablespoons shelled shrimps; 2 tablespoons sultanas; 1 tablespoon finely diced sweet apple. Reheat gently until all the ingredients are hot. Finally, just before serving, stir in 1 tablespoon of any fruity bottled sauce or chutney or tomato ketchup, and serve at once.

## GOLDEN BAKE

This is a very savoury dish, and you can either eat it as a snack on its own, or serve it as the potato part of an ordinary meal. If you're going to eat it as part of a meal, you need to begin preparing it well in advance, about an hour and a half before the meal.

Butter a shallow, ovenproof dish. Peel some raw potatoes and slice them thinly, and cover the base of the dish with a layer of potatoes. Peel some raw onions and slice them thinly, and cover the potatoes with a layer of sliced onions. Then give a liberal shake of salt and pepper, and add a few scraps of butter to the dish. Repeat this double layer at least once, twice more for a very large family or a substantial snack! Next, add a final layer of sliced potatoes, and pour on enough milk to come just below the top layer of potato slices. Put in the oven, at 325 deg. or gas mark 3, with a piece of metal foil across the top of the dish. After an hour, turn the heat up to 400 deg., gas mark 6, and remove the foil, so the top will turn a lovely golden brown in about 20 minutes more cooking.

We must be thankful, Joan. We shall spend a warmer night than our poor Queen Matilda trapped in Oxford Castle, there. Her supplies of food and firewood must be spent.

Why do the barons hunt her down, father? After all, she is the Queen of England!

When King Henry lay dying the great lords promised they would support his daughter and now they turn against her!

But there were many who did not want a woman on the throne of England and when Matilda proved so proud and haughty they turned to her cousin Stephen.

Look, the soldiers are walking on the river.

I fear it is the end for Queen Matilda. If the ice is firm enough Stephen will lead his army across the river and take the castle. Go home quickly, Joan, the river bank is no place for children now!

I've used the last of the turnips in this broth—I pray that father will be successful in the market—he's been away a long time.

*The day wore on and still Dan Beckett did not return—*

Stephen's men have crossed the river—if he captures the Queen he will have no mercy! I'm glad that Robin is sleeping safely at home—oh, hurry, father!

Here are four monks from Osney Abbey—what can they be doing on the river?

*Suddenly—*

Father! I didn't hear your footsteps in the snow! Did you sell the rabbits at the market?

No, Stephen's soldiers took me prisoner and stole them from me—the army is hungry too! I managed to escape—quick, we must get home!

*But then—*

Wait, peasants!

It is the monks, I saw them coming across the river from the castle.

**Quick, girl, lead us to food and shelter or your father dies!**

**Please don't hurt him, I'll do as you say!**

**These men are not holy fathers!**

*Later—* **Hurry girl, serve out this broth!**

**You are welcome to it, only please, I beg you, leave a drop for my little brother — he has not eaten today!**

**Wait! I will not have you frighten children in my name! Bring the little one to me!**

**That is the voice of a woman!**

**I am Matilda, your Queen. I know now that my pride has brought about my downfall and I ask you humbly if I may shelter here and beg a bowl of broth.**

**My Lady, we will do anything to help you! Only, please, I beg you, release my father from his bonds!**

**If you will keep the Queen hidden here, two of us can go to Abingdon where some friends have promised us horses.**

**I will guard her with my life!**

**I must leave England now, Joan, and seek refuge with my friends in Normandy. But I shall not forget this night and how the poorest of my subjects shared a bowl of broth with me.**

*Later—* **Goodbye! Oh, father, will they ever reach safety?**

**The great barons will scour the countryside, but there are many humble folk who will help her Majesty on her way!**

*Matilda made good her escape to Normandy and her cousin Stephen became King of England. But the Queen never forgot the escape and she sent a grant of money, " For poor people living by the river to comfort them in cold weather."*

Can we manage here? I-I'm living in one room.

Good idea! These old houses are far too big.

Is she here all alone? It's so creepy and gloomy.

Your hair is very fine—and so tangled! I'll have to use a conditioner or it will never comb out.

Please do what you like with it. I'm very tired . . .

She's so pale and slender. I wonder if she eats enough? There doesn't seem to be any food here.

I have a packet of sandwiches in my mo-ped. Like to share them?

How very kind of you!

Somebody at the door by the sound of it. I'll see to it!

Odd! There's nobody here, Mo. Oh well—let's eat. This hill-top air is making me hungry.

But—

Hello! I'm back! Where are you?

*After ten minutes—*

The Case of the Vanishing Client, Mo! I've called and searched but there's no sign of her. No point in wasting more time here.

*Jo took another road downhill and . . .*

Hey! Stop! Are you Jo Jenner?

My sister is waiting for you to set her hair. She booked by telephone. Did you have a breakdown on your bike?

No. I was held up though. You'd better lead the way.

EYRIE HOUSE

Another Eyrie House! What's going on?

I'm Daisy Harker. I'm glad you found me. The telephone line was so bad that I was afraid you hadn't heard clearly.

Well, I was confused, Daisy. I went to Eyrie House at the very top of the hill!

I'm sorry you had a wasted journey. The old house has been empty for years.

A girl was there. I thought she rang me. I was going to set her hair but—she disappeared! Vanished into thin air. It was sort of ghostly.

That's exactly what that girl was—a ghost! Old Eyrie House is haunted!

WH-WHAT?

I'm Katie Gray. I ran away from home. There were rows... I can't cope with life. I always make mistakes. I'm hopeless!

Nobody is hopeless. What you need is a fresh start. And first you've got to have a new image. I'll fetch my case and show you what I mean.

I'll shape your hair into a neat, easy to manage, style

I won't argue, Jo.

It's amazing. I look efficient and capable.

Then you've a head start to a better life! You can't float around forever like a fairy princess from the past.

That reminds me... Did you really think I was a ghost?

Well—my clients don't usually vanish! But I knew you had a real head on your shoulders, Katie. There's one strange thing though...

That knocking at the door. There was nobody there!

Oooh— let's go. I've had enough of this house!

*A few weeks later—*

Katie's a lot smarter since we found her, Mo. She hadn't the ghost of a chance of success with her life in tangles- or her hair.

# TEASER TIME

*Charlie Chaplin* (handwritten)

Can you help this silent movie star through the maze? Also, can you say what his name was?

*paperclip* (handwritten)

A picture of an object has been cut into four different pieces. Can you guess what the object is? *6* (handwritten)

Out of all these bits and pieces, can you tell how many cup-and-ball games can be made up? *3* (handwritten)

These nine little men look alike, but one is slightly different from the others. Which one?

*cheese knife* (handwritten)

This common household article has been photographed from an odd angle. What is it?

## ANSWERS

MAZE:—Charlie Chaplin
PICTURE PUZZLE:— Paperclip.
CUP AND BALL:—3.
NINE LITTLE MEN:—6. He
has left ear missing.
PHOTOGRAPH:—Cheese knife.

# Lonely Carol

I SUPPOSE everyone likes to have a really special friend, and Carol was no exception . . .

Oh, Carol! You've hardly given it a chance. Today was only your first day at your new school, remember.

But it's—it's so big, Mum. I'll never make any friends there, I just know it. I-I can't even find my way around, not properly.

Mum just doesn't understand. Oh, I wish we'd never had to leave the village. The—the girls were far more friendly there.

Next day—

Whoops! Oo, sorry!

It's all right. You're Carol, aren't you? The new girl?

Bet you're finding it all a bit strange. I know I did, the first few days.

Yes! Yes I am, rather.

Look, why don't you come across and join me and the gang at break? I mean, sort of get to know people?

Gosh, that's really nice of you. I'd like that.

That's wonderful! I've got a friend.

We always stay to watch the netball match after school.

Oh, so will I, then. That'll be great, Wendy.

Carol enjoyed watching the game with her new friend.

Sit there by Carol, Jayne. She'll look after you.

Huh, she looks even more miserable than I did. Why do I have to be lumbered with her?

Oh, no! Here she comes again. She keeps following me about like a shadow.

I-I'm sorry, Carol. I seem to have lost my way again.

Carol if you could just tell me which exercise we have to do for home-work, please. I-I just didn't understand what Miss Boyd said, look.

Oh, for goodness sake! I wish you'd just stop hanging round me!

Oh, dear. I shouldn't have said it. But—but I don't want to be friends with another new girl. Not now I've got Wendy.

But a day or so later—

Oh Wendy, there you are. I thought we were walking back together.

What? Oh, yes. Sorry. It's just that Jayne, here was having trouble with her maths. I said I'd go back to her house and give her a hand. She lives quite near me.

Carol stalked off, furious with Wendy and even more furious with Jayne.

How could she? I mean, surely Wendy can see she's just trying to break us up. Golly, I'm jolly well not speaking to her tomorrow. And as for that grotty Jayne . . .

SHEILA HAWKINS and Jean Marsh often helped out in an antique shop owned by Sheila's uncle. The girls had discovered that Sheila's torch had a magical lens which could transport them back through time, when its light shone on anything with an unusual history . . .

# The Shop at Shudder Corner

It's safe to go to your workshop now, Uncle. Then you won't see what we break when we're dusting.

I'll try not to believe you!

Fantastic! Just look at that lovely old model in the bottle.

It's a beauty! I've always wondered how they got the ship inside.

There's one sure way to find out. Let's try a little more light on the subject.

No, Sheila . . . not your torch! You always make something frightening happen.

I only wanted to read the name on the ship . . . oooh!

Everything's spinning! I knew you'd do it!

We're at sea! You-you idiot! We're adrift with no land in sight!

I didn't mean it, Jean.

You could get us both drowned. We could be anywhere.

Use the oars! Quick, make us head into the waves. We'll capsize if we're hit by another vessel broadside on.

Minutes later—

A ship! A ship! Make them see us. They'll pick us up.

Now it makes sense. It's just like the model in the bottle!

The girls shouted and waved, for all they were worth—

They've seen us! It's turning towards us.

Thank goodness for that. The first lucky adventure we've ever had.

Sheila! It's not stopping! Not slowing! We'll be rammed.

Use the oar! Pull . . . pull! Try to get to one side.

*With a sickening thud, the sailing ship rammed the little boat—*

AAAAAAGH!

That rope! Grab for it! Quick!

Hang on . . . !

Where is everyone? Haven't they seen us? Can't someone give us a hand?

Ahoy there! . . . Help!

There's no one! It seems completely deserted.

I don't like it. I'm scared. Try using the torch to take us back to our own time.

It won't work! I can't get a light!

We're stranded with miles of ocean around us. I'm freezing cold too.

Come on, let's go below. It's a bit creepy.

Don't leave me behind. I hate to see that wheel turning by itself.

Help me! I'll try to turn the wheel!

On board the other ship—

My oath! There he is at the wheel . . .

We're going to crash!

I'll try the torch! Please, please let it work!

And—

It worked! The narrow beam came on!

Next moment . . .

Ah, the model of the famous ghost ship —the old 'Flying Dutchman.' The story goes that its captain, Vanderdecken, was cursed to sail the seven seas until Judgement Day . . .

A phantom vessel that rises from the waves and is generally an omen of disaster. There are several quite well authenticated reports. It was once even seen by King George V.

Wow! I wonder who saw us? I mean, you looked a pretty crazy figure in that old seaman's coat!

Oh, no! They couldn't have thought I was old Captain Vanderdecken, could they? Sheila Hawkins, that's a rotten idea!

# LITTLE SIS

Maisie, come down off the wall—you'll fall!
Oh, no I won't. I'm good at this—
EEK! Well usually I am.

UGH!

Ho-ho! A mud pack's very good for your skin, Debbie!

That was a stupid thing to do. Climbing on walls is dangerous. You shouldn't ever do it.

HMMM!

You really mustn't ever do that again . . .!

Hey, Debbie, look—a worm!

EEK!

Debbie! Come down off that wall. You ought to know better!

TEE-HEE!

# Debbie Superpets

# No Sympathy

"**L**OOK!**"** I said to Sandie. " **Did you see that?"** I pulled my sister's wheelchair close to the wall, bending towards her as I pointed.

She stared with lack-lustre eyes, not answering. She'd been like this ever since the road accident, and there was nothing Mum or I could do to shake her out of it. They'd said at the hospital she was getting better, that she'd soon be able to walk again, but nothing seemed to cure her awful depression. She just wasn't interested in anything.

# for Sandie...

Through the gap in the trees, the hang-glider seemed to float through the air, knees bent, arms outstretched, like a huge, graceful bird.

"He must have taken off from Gallows Hill," I said. "The wind's brought him down here."

I might have been talking to myself for all the interest Sandie took.

"If we go closer we can see him float over the downs," I went on.

I pushed the chair over the lane, careful not to jar Sandie's legs. For a moment I wished I hadn't suggested it remembering how keen on sport Sandie had been She'd always been the outgoing type, anxious to try anything new.

I often thought to myself that she'd convinced herself she'd never be able to join in things again, that she'd just shut her mind to everything.

When we reached the gap in the trees, the hang-glider seemed to be hovering, motionless, in the air. He wasn't flying too high, but it was still thrilling to watch.

"Oh, isn't it super?" I said. "Don't you wish that—"

"It's cold here," she said abruptly. "Let's go home."

"Oh, Sandie . . . "

An awful feeling of real despair swept over me. I hated to see her like this. Even though there was quite a big gap between us—nearly four years—we'd always been pretty close.

"All right," I agreed.

I began to turn the wheelchair. And then it happened!

One moment he was hanging there, suspended, and the next moment, quite suddenly, he'd plunged straight to the ground.

"He-he's fallen! Sandie, he's fallen!"

For a moment I just didn't know what to do. Then I began pushing the wheelchair, haphazardly, breathlessly, towards him.

**W**HEN we reached him, he was lying quite motionless in the tangle of his glider, his legs tucked under him. Helplessly, I stared down, not knowing if I should try to move him or not.

And then I heard my sister's voice from behind me, crisp and authoritative.

"Put your jacket under his head, Jackie," she said.

"And push some of that material away, so that he can breathe."

She propelled the wheelchair as close to us as she could, giving instructions all the time.

It was just like the old Sandie. As I smoothed the boy's hair from his forehead, his eyelids fluttered open.

"Crikey, that was some landing!" he said. He tried to sit up, and I helped him. "No bones broken, anyway," he added, sounding a bit shaky.

"You'd better stop there for a while," my sister said.

He seemed to see her for the first time. And it was strange, because even from that very moment, he knew just how to treat her.

"You could lend me that wheelchair," he joked. "You don't look as if you really need it."

"I don't," she said, instantly, almost angrily.

And then she laughed.

Honestly, I couldn't believe it. It was the first time I'd heard her do that since—well, since before that awful car crash.

"Well, I do for a bit longer," she admitted.

The boy scrambled to his feet.

"You recover very quickly," Sandie said. She was still smiling.

"Oh, yeah. Tarzan, that's me." He began gathering up his glider.

"Just about made a mess of this though," he muttered.

Then, as a thought seemed to strike him: "You wouldn't carry it across your wheelchair for me, would you? Till we get back on the road? I mean, I'll push you. I don't live very far away."

"Cheek," Sandie retorted. "Well, okay, then."

I stared, almost open-mouthed. Neither of them took any notice of me. I trailed along beside them. Not that I cared. I hadn't felt so happy for weeks as I listened to them.

The boy was actually telling Sandie he'd teach her to hang-glide. Not when she was better, but when he became more expert. It was as if her being in a wheelchair meant nothing at all!

Quite suddenly I knew where we'd gone wrong. We'd been treating Sandie like the invalid she thought she was, instead of a normal person. It'd taken a stranger to bring her out of her self-pity.

The only thing was, I didn't think by the way that he and my sister were looking at each other that he was going to be a stranger for very much longer . . .

# Jaguar Girl

Carole Buckle little imagined a career as a mechanic when she joined the Women's Royal Air Force. Aptitude tests showed her to be suitable, though, and always ready for a challenge, Carole decided to give it a try.

A posting to R.A.F. Abingdon followed the completion of her basic training and Carole was soon working on aircraft under the watchful eye of her instructor.

Imagine her surprise when she discovered that there were two other girl mechanics, Wendy and Susan, at the air base.

Carole's work specialises mainly in the structure of the Jaguar aircraft together with such things as hydraulic systems, landing gear and flying controls.

A pilot's life might depend on the skill of mechanics such as Carole, and her work must be of the highest standard.

While Carole works on another part of the aircraft, Wendy and Susan get on with refuelling the plane's tanks.

It's a dirty job, as you can see, but it's also a very worthwhile and rewarding one.

CLEAN FUEL ONLY
CONTAINER TO BE INSPECTED
BEFORE USE

Here, Carole and Wendy tend to a problem in the cockpit of a Jaguar.

None of the girls regrets joining the WRAF. There's a very hectic social life with discos, dances and clubs and the opportunity is also there for travelling to places like Germany and Cyprus.

Owl's nest was empty— Dad looked. His mother and brothers and sisters have gone away. Never mind, Owl. You'll have a home when you come out of hospital, with me.

Owl will have to stay here for quite some time, Sarah.

The weeks passed, and Sarah was a daily visitor. The owl flourished and grew strong

We'll discharge him as soon as he's learned to fly. Teaching him will take time and patience.

We've plenty of patience, sir. It's time we're short on.

I'll teach him at home. Mummy and Daddy said I could ask you if it was all right to take Owl home. We've got a big garden and it's quiet there, near the fields and the woods. Please say I may!

Hmm . . . it would be just until he can fly, Sarah. Then he should go back to the woods, and to his own kind.

All right—if he wants to. But I don't suppose he will.

It's possible that he will become completely domesticated, happy to live in a house. I've known it happen with other wild birds.

Sarah took Owl home and later, Jill called at Sarah's home to see how he was getting on.

Hello, there. Hey, that's a fine dog, Sarah!

His name is Jack, and he's super. He and Owl are friends. Come on, Owl. Show Jill how well you can fly.

Owl flew round the room, then settled on Sarah's shoulder.

That's his favourite perch.

He likes to sit on Jack's back, too, and Jack gives him rides. He's very happy, Nurse Jill.

And yet there's something in his eyes . . . oh, perhaps I'm imagining it.

The Easter chick with shining eyes
Wears a coat of yellow down.
He'll peck and cheep, for all his size,
As he scurries all around.